I WILL BUILD YOU A HOUSE

A cornucopia of poems to delight readers of
all ages but particularly for the very young.
From Robert Louis Stevenson and Charles
Causley to Spike Milligan and Anon.
Dorothy Butler has brought together her
second marvellous poetry collection, an entire
poetry house.

Dorothy Butler runs a children's bookshop in Auckland, New Zealand which includes a reading service, and edits and writes children's books. In 1979, she was awarded the Eleanor Farjeon Award for services to children's literature. *Cushla and her Books* (published by Hodder and Stoughton, 1979) which earned her that award, was based on a study of her severely handicapped granddaughter. *Babies Need Books* (published by Penguin), Dorothy Butler's best selling guide to introducing the very young to books and reading, has been followed by *Five to Eight*.

I will build you a house

Poems
chosen by

DOROTHY BUTLER

Illustrated by Megan Gressor

KNIGHT BOOKS
Hodder and Stoughton

For Cushla and Sanchia

Copyright © for each poem remains
with the author, 1984
Copyright © for this collection
Dorothy Butler, 1984
Copyright © for illustrations Hodder
and Stoughton (Australia) Pty Limited,
1984

First published in 1984 by Hodder and
Stoughton (Australia) Pty Limited

First published in Great Britain by
Knight Books, 1988

British Library C.I.P.

I will build you a house : poems.
1. Poetry in English – Anthologies
I. Butler, Dorothy II. Gressor, Megan
821'.008

ISBN 0 340 49514 6

Printed and bound in Great Britain
for Hodder and Stoughton
Paperbacks, a division of Hodder and
Stoughton Ltd., Mill Road,
Dunton Green, Sevenoaks, Kent
TN13 2YA. (Editorial Office:
47 Bedford Square, London
WC1B 3DP) by Cox & Wyman Ltd.,
Reading

CONTENTS

INTRODUCTION

I have known many of the poems in this collection for so long that I cannot judge them: just love them, which is the best way with poems, and people, too.

Walter de la Mare's "Silver" was the first poem I ever learned by heart at school, when I was about six. I think that I have looked at the night with different eyes, ever since. This is one of the things that poetry does for you, of course. It almost *tricks* you into seeing.

People do not often grow up to love poetry unless they have learned to enjoy it as children. They are the lucky ones who learn early that poetry involves a special way of using ordinary words so as to bring pictures to the mind's eye, and that feelings aroused by a good poem bring understanding faster and more surely than a whole prose book on the same subject.

In our world of strident sound and flashing light, most children have little hope of making these discoveries unless adults come to their assistance. Reading poetry aloud is the very best way to do this.

I Will Build You a House contains those poems which I most like to read to children between six and twelve. The degree of understanding varies, of course, with age and experience but I have found that the youngest will happily absorb what they can, and let the rest flow warmly around them.

Like its predecessor *For Me, Me, Me*, this second

volume does not pretend to be a "balanced" collection. Over a long period of time its various poems, hand-copied, came to live together in an ancient folder which also housed the verses for younger children. When the inhabitants of that comfortable refuge increased to insupportable numbers and it finally crumbled at the seams, a new, separate home was found for each group.

I have never liked my poetry divided into "topics" or "themes" and have never found a child who did either. I like poems to spring at me unawares, and I don't like other people to tell me what they are about. I have allowed the poems in this book to fall almost as they would. I like them that way, and I think that children will too.

Some people are sure to say that a few of the poems are sentimental, and that more than a few of them are hackneyed. Well, so are many of the things that are good in this world, and everything is new to each successive wave of young people.

I believe that children need idealism as well as realism. Along with their undoubted resilience goes intense sensitivity, and the need to strive for things that are good and true. With just a little help, they will look and laugh and love and learn with astonishing, almost limitless energy and faith.

Poetry will help them to do all these things even better.

Dorothy Butler

ENVOY

Go, little book, and wish to all
Flowers in the garden, meat in the hall,
A bin of wine, a spice of wit,
A house with lawns enclosing it,
A living river by the door,
A nightingale in the sycamore!

Robert Louis Stevenson

LITTLE GIRL

I will build you a house
If you do not cry,
A house, little girl,
As tall as the sky.

I will build you a house
Of golden dates,
The freshest of all
For the steps and gates.

I will furnish the house,
For you and for me
With walnuts and hazels
Fresh from the tree.

I will build you a house,
And when it is done
I will roof it with grapes
To keep out the sun.

Rose Fyleman

ADVENTURE

It's not very far
   to the edge of town
Where trees look up
   and hills look down.
We go there
   almost every day
To climb and swing
   and paddle and play.

It's not very far
   to the edge of town
Just up one little
   hill and down,
And through one gate,
   and over two stiles —
But coming home
   it's miles and miles.

Harry Behn   ## LITTLE WIND

Little wind, blow on the hill-top,
Little wind, blow down the plain;
Little wind, blow up the sunshine,
Little wind, blow off the rain.

Kate Greenaway

VIOLETS, DAFFODILS . . .

Violets, daffodils,
Roses and thorn
Were all in the garden
Before you were born.

Daffodils, violets,
Green thorn and roses
Your grandchildren's children
Will hold to their noses.

Elizabeth Coatsworth

PRAYER OF THE BRETON FISHERMAN

Dear God,
Be good to me.

The sea is so wide
And my boat is so small.

Anon

I SAW A JOLLY HUNTER

I saw a jolly hunter
    With a jolly gun
Walking in the country
    In the jolly sun.

In the jolly meadow
    Sat a jolly hare.
Saw the jolly hunter.
    Took jolly care.

Hunter jolly eager —
    Sight of jolly prey.
Forgot gun pointing
    Wrong jolly way.

Jolly hunter jolly head
    Over heels gone.
Jolly old safety-catch
    Not jolly on.

Bang went the jolly gun.
    Hunter jolly dead.
Jolly hare got clean away.
    Jolly good, I said.

Charles Causley

DREAM VARIATION

To fling my arms wide
In some place in the sun,
To whirl and to dance
Till the white day is done.
Then rest at cool evening
Beneath a tall tree
While night comes on gently,
  Dark like me —
That is my dream!

To fling my arms wide
In the face of the sun,
Dance! Whirl! Whirl!
Till the quick day is done
Rest at pale evening . . .
A tall, slim tree . . .
Night coming tenderly,
  Black like me.

Langston Hughes

WHO'S IN?

"The door is shut fast
And everyone's out."
But people don't know
What they're talking about!
Say the fly on the wall,
And the flame on the coals
And the dog on his rug,
And the mice in their holes,
And the kitten curled up,
And the spiders that spin —
    "What, everyone out?
    Why, everyone's in!"

Elizabeth Fleming

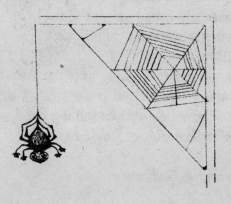

EAT AWAY, CHEW AWAY

Eat away, chew away, munch and
                                bolt and guzzle.
Never leave the table till you're full
                                up to the muzzle.

  Norman Lindsay

I MEANT TO DO MY WORK TODAY

I meant to do my work today —
But a brown bird sang in the apple tree,
And a butterfly flitted across the field,
And all the leaves were calling me.

And the wind went sighing over the land,
Tossing the grasses to and fro,
And a rainbow held out its shining hand —
So what could I do but laugh and go?

  Richard le Gallienne

IF I WERE A TREE

If I were a tree
   like you,
Instead of a child
   like me,
I would dig my roots
   in the good black earth
And toss my arms
   to the sea.
I would be twisted and small
   like you
For the winds
   to bend me low
And drops of rain on my twigs
   would lie
Like silver beads
   in a row.
I would be like you
   as ever I could —
Green-spiked
   and needle-y,
If I were a little tree
   like you,
Instead of a child
   like me!

Rachel Field

PLEA

From ghoulies and ghosties,
Long-legged beasties,
And things that go bump in the night,
Good Lord, deliver us.

Anon

WINDY NIGHTS

Rumbling in the chimneys,
    Rattling at the doors,
Round the roofs and round the roads
    The rude wind roars;
Raging through the darkness,
    Raving through the trees,
Racing off again across
    The great grey seas.

Rodney Bennett

GENERAL STORE

Some day I'm going
  to have a store
With a tinkly bell
  hung over the door,
With real glass cases
  and counters wide
And drawers all spilly
  with things inside.
There'll be a little
  of everything:
Bolts of calico;
  balls of string;
Jars of peppermint;
  tins of tea;

Pots and kettles
  and crockery;
Seeds in packets;
  scissors bright;
Bags of sugar,
  brown and white;
Sarsaparilla
  for picnic lunches,
Bananas and
  rubber boots in bunches.
I'll fix the window
  and dust each shelf,
And take the money in
  all myself.
It will be my store
  and I will say:
"What can I do
  for you today?"

Rachel Field

19

TABLE MANNERS

The Goops they lick their fingers,
And the Goops they lick their knives;
They spill their broth on the table-cloth;
Oh, they lead disgusting lives!
The Goops they talk while eating,
And loud and fast they chew;
So that is why I'm glad that I
Am not a Goop. Are you?

Gelett Burgess

APRIL RAIN SONG

Let the rain kiss you.
Let the rain beat upon your head with
                              silver liquid drops.
Let the rain sing you a lullaby.

The rain makes still pools on the sidewalk.
The rain makes running pools in the gutter.
The rain plays a little sleep-song on our
                              roof at night —

And I love the rain.

Langston Hughes

LULLABY OF AN INFANT CHIEF

O hush thee, my baby, thy sire was a knight,
Thy mother a lady, both lovely and bright;
The woods and the glens, from the towers which we see,
They all are belonging, dear baby, to thee.

O fear not the bugle, though loudly it blows,
It calls but the warders that guard thy repose;
Their bows would be bended, their blades would be red,
Ere the step of a foeman draw near to thy bed.

O hush thee, my baby, the time will come soon,
When thy sleep shall be broken by trumpet and drum;
Then hush thee, my darling, take rest while you may,
For strife comes with manhood, and waking with day.

Sir Walter Scott

21

THE PRAYER OF THE LITTLE DUCKS

Dear God,
give us a flood of water.
Let it rain tomorrow and always.
Give us plenty of little slugs
and other luscious things to eat.
Protect all folk who quack
and everyone who knows how to swim.

Carmen Bernos de Gasztold,
translated by Rumer Godden

THE FALLOW DEER AT THE LONELY HOUSE

One without looks in tonight
  Through the curtain-chink
From the sheet of glistening white;
One without looks in tonight
  As we sit and think
  By the fender-brink.

We do not discern those eyes
  Watching in the snow;
Lit by lamps of rosy dyes
We do not discern those eyes
  Wondering, aglow,
  Four-footed, tiptoe.

Thomas Hardy

CAT'S FUNERAL

Bury her deep, down deep,
Safe in the earth's cold keep,
Bury her deep —

No more to watch bird stir;
No more to clean dark fur;
No more to glisten as silk;
No more to revel in milk;
No more to purr.

Bury her deep, down deep;
She is beyond warm sleep.
She will not walk in the night;
She will not wake to the light.
Bury her deep.

E. V. Rieu

FULL OF THE MOON

It's full of the moon
The dogs dance out
Through brush and bush and bramble.
They howl and yowl
And growl and prowl.
They amble ramble scramble.
They rush through brush.
They push through bush.
They yip and yap and hurr.
They lark around and bark around
With prickles in their fur.
They two-step in the meadow.
They polka on the lawn.
Tonight's the night
The dogs dance out
And chase their tails till dawn.

Karla Kuskin

FOR A BIRD

I found him lying near the tree; I folded
                              up his wings.
Oh, little bird, you never heard
The song the summer sings.

I wrapped him in a shirt I wore in
                              winter; it was blue.

Oh, little bird,
You never heard
The song I sang to you.

Myra Cohn Livingston

A CHRISTMAS CAROL

The Christ-child lay on Mary's lap,
His hair was like a light.
(O weary weary were the world,
But here is all aright.)

The Christ-child lay on Mary's breast,
His hair was like a star.
(O stern and cunning are the kings,
But here the true hearts are.)

The Christ-child lay on Mary's heart,
His hair was like a fire.
(O weary weary is the world,
But here the world's desire.)

The Christ-child stood at Mary's knee,
His hair was like a crown,
And all the flowers looked up at Him,
And all the stars looked down.

G. K. Chesterton

EVER

Ever, ever
Stir and shiver
The reeds and rushes
By the river:
Ever, ever,
As in a dream,
The lone moon's silver
Sleeks the stream.
What old sorrow,
What lost love,
Moon, reeds, rushes,
Dream you of ?

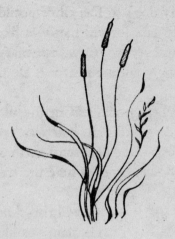

Walter de la Mare

A SMALL PRAYER

Dear Father, hear and bless
Thy beasts and singing birds
And guard with tenderness
Small things that have no words.

Anon

THE HAIRY DOG

My dog's so furry I've not seen
His face for years and years:
His eyes are buried out of sight,
I only guess his ears.

When people ask me for his breed,
I do not know or care:
He has the beauty of them all
Hidden beneath his hair.

Herbert Asquith

A WARNING

If you should meet a crocodile
    Don't take a stick and poke him;
Ignore the welcome in his smile,
    Be careful not to stroke him.
For as he sleeps upon the Nile,
    He thinner gets and thinner;
And whene'er you meet a crocodile
    He's ready for his dinner.

Anon

JENNY KISSED ME

Jenny kissed me when we met,
Jumping from the chair she sat in;
Time, you thief, who love to get
Sweets into your list, put that in:
Say I'm weary, say I'm sad,
Say that health and wealth have missed me,
Say I'm growing old, but add,
Jenny kissed me.

Leigh Hunt

GOOD SENSE

Hearts, like doors,
open with ease
to very very little keys.

And don't forget
that two of these
are, "I thank you"
and
"If you please".

Anon

THE ANIMAL STORE

If I had a hundred dollars to spend,
Or maybe a little more,
I'd hurry as fast as my legs would go
Straight to the animal store.

I wouldn't say, "How much for this or that?" —
"What kind of a dog is he?"
I'd buy as many as rolled an eye,
Or wagged a tail at me!

I'd take the hound with the drooping ears
That sits by himself alone;
Cockers and Cairns and wobbly pups
For to be my very own.

I might buy a parrot all red and green,
And a monkey I saw before,
If I had a hundred dollars to spend,
Or maybe a little more.

Rachel Field

HURT NO LIVING THING

Hurt no living thing:
  Ladybird, nor butterfly,
Nor moth with dusty wing,
  Nor cricket chirping cheerily,
Nor grasshopper, so light of leap,
  Nor dancing gnat, nor beetle fat,
Nor harmless worms that creep.

   Christina Rossetti

MY HEART LEAPS UP

My heart leaps up when I behold
  A rainbow in the sky:
So was it when my life began;
So is it now I am a man;
So be it when I shall grow old,
Or let me die!

   William Wordsworth

A CRADLE SONG

O men from the fields!
Come gently within,
Tread softly, softly,
O men coming in!

Mavourneen is going
From me and from you,
Where Mary will fold him
With mantle of blue!

From reek of the smoke
And cold of the floor,
And the peerings of things
Across the half-door.

O men from the fields!
Soft, softly come through —
Mary puts round him
Her mantle of blue.

Padraic Colum

EPITAPH FOR A PERSIAN KITTEN

Death, who one day taketh all,
Wise or good or great or small,
Every creature of the air,
Every creature of the sea,
All life here and everywhere,
What is thine we give to thee.
Neither great nor very wise,
Yet beloved in our eyes,
   Lightly hold and gently keep
   A small good kitten in her sleep.

Miriam Vedder

IF ONCE YOU HAVE SLEPT ON
AN ISLAND . . .

If once you have slept on an island
You'll never be quite the same;
You may look as you looked the day before
And go by the same old name,

You may bustle about in street or shop
You may sit at home and sew
But you'll see blue water and wheeling gulls
Wherever your feet may go.

You may chat with the neighbours of this and that
And close to your fire keep
But you'll hear ship whistle and lighthouse bell
And tides beat through your sleep.

Oh, you won't know why and you can't say how
Such change upon you came,
But — once you have slept on an island
You'll never be quite the same!

Rachel Field

CONFUSION

There once was a simple marine,
Whose musical sense was not keen.
He said "It is odd,
I cannot tell 'God
Save the Weasel' from
'Pop Goes the Queen' ".

Anon

I HEARD A BIRD SING

I heard a bird sing
    In the dark of December
A magical thing
    And sweet to remember.

"We are nearer to spring
    Than we were in September,"
I heard a bird sing
    In the dark of December.

Oliver Herford

36

WHO HAS SEEN THE WIND?

Who has seen the wind?
Neither I nor you:
But when the leaves hang trembling
The wind is passing thro'.

Who has seen the wind?
Neither you nor I:
But when the trees bow down their heads
The wind is passing by.

Christina Rossetti

BLESSINGS

God bless all those that I love,
God bless all those that love me.
God bless all those that love
      those that I love,
And those that love those
      that love me!

Anon

THE LAMPLIGHTER

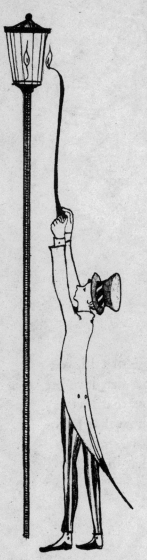

My tea is nearly ready
   and the sun has left the sky.
It's time to take the window
   to see Leerie going by;
For every night at tea-time
   and before you take your seat,
With lantern and with ladder
   he comes posting up the street.

Now Tom would be a driver
   and Maria go to sea,
And my papa's a banker
   and as rich as he can be;
But I, when I am stronger
   and can choose what I'm to do,
O Leerie, I'll go round at night
   and light the lamps with you!

For we are very lucky,
   with a lamp before the door,
And Leerie stops to light it
   as he lights so many more;
And oh! before you hurry by
   with ladder and with light,
O Leerie, see a little child
   and nod to him tonight!

Robert Louis Stevenson

LESSON

To plant a seed
  and see it grow
Is something every
  child should do,
And when it blossoms,
  how it grew
Is something every
  child should know,
And when its seeds
  are ripe to sow
A child may see
  the old made new.
To grow and gently
  grow and grow
Is something people
  should do too.

Harry Behn

LONG, LONG AGO

Winds through the olive trees
Softly did blow
Round little Bethlehem
Long, long ago.

Sheep on the hillside lay
Whiter than snow;
Shepherds were watching them,
Long, long ago.

Then from the happy sky
Angels bent low,
Singing their songs of joy,
Long, long ago.

For in a manger bed
Cradled, we know
Christ came to Bethlehem,
Long, long ago.

Anon

A MEMORY

This I remember,
I saw from a train:
A shaggy wild pony
That stood in the rain.

Where I was going,
And where was the train,
I cannot remember,
I cannot explain.

All these years after
It comes back again:
A shaggy wild pony
That stood in the rain.

Douglas Gibson

ELETELEPHONY

Once there was an elephant
Who tried to use the telephant —
No! No! I mean an elephone
Who tried to use the telephone —
(Dear me! I am not certain quite
That even now I've got it right.)

Howe'er it was, he got his trunk
Entangled in the telephunk;
The more he tried to get it free,
The louder buzzed the telephee —
(I fear I'd better drop the song
Of elephop and telephong!)

Laura E. Richards

THE TIDE IN THE RIVER

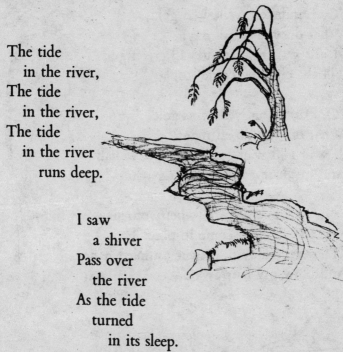

The tide
  in the river,
The tide
  in the river,
The tide
  in the river
    runs deep.

    I saw
      a shiver
    Pass over
      the river
    As the tide
      turned
        in its sleep.

Eleanor Farjeon

THE DANDELION

"O, Dandelion, yellow as gold,
What do you do all day?"
"I just wait here in the tall green grass
Till the children come to play."

"O, Dandelion, yellow as gold,
What do you do all night?"
"I wait and wait till the cool dews fall
And my hair grows long and white."

"And what do you do when your hair is white
And the children come to play?"
"They take me up in their dimpled hands,
And blow my hair away."

Anon

RAIN

The rain it raineth on the just
And also on the unjust fella:
But chiefly on the just, because
The unjust steals the just's umbrella.

Charles Bowen

THE WIND

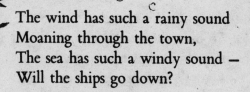

The wind has such a rainy sound
Moaning through the town,
The sea has such a windy sound —
Will the ships go down?

The apples in the orchard
Tumble from their tree —
Oh, will the ships go down, go down,
In the windy sea?

Christina Rossetti

DISGUISE

There once was a maiden called Maggie,
Whose dog was enormous and shaggy,
The front end of him
Looked vicious and grim —
But the back end was friendly and waggy.

Anon

AN OLD WOMAN OF THE ROADS

O, to have a little house!
    To own the hearth and stool and all!
The heaped-up sods upon the fire,
    The pile of turf against the wall!

To have a clock with weights and chains
    And pendulum swinging up and down!
A dresser filled with shining delph,
    Speckled and white and blue and brown!

I could be busy all the day
    Clearing and sweeping hearth and floor,
And fixing on their shelf again
    My white and blue and speckled store!

I could be quiet there at night
    Beside the fire and by myself,
Sure of a bed, and loth to leave
    The ticking clock and shining delph!

Och! but I'm weary of mist and dark,
    And roads where there's never a house or bush
And tired I am of bog and road
    And the crying wind and lonesome hush!

And I am praying to God on high,
    And I am praying Him night and day,
For a little house — a house of my own —
    Out of the wind's and the rain's way.

Padraic Colum

HOLD FAST YOUR DREAMS

Within your heart
Keep one still, secret spot
Where dreams may go,
And sheltered so,
May thrive and grow —
Where doubt and fear are not.
Oh, keep a place apart
Within your heart,
For little dreams to go.

Louise Driscoll

THE NIGHT WILL NEVER STAY

The night will never stay,
The night will still go by,
Though with a million stars
You pin it to the sky.
Though you bind it with the blowing wind
And buckle it with the moon,
The night will slip away
Like sorrow or a tune.

Eleanor Farjeon

A LITTLE SONG OF LIFE

Glad that I live am I;
That the sky is blue;
Glad for the country lanes,
And the fall of dew.

After the sun the rain;
After rain the sun;
This is the way of life
Till the work be done.

All that we need to do,
Be we low or high,
Is to see that we grow
Nearer the sky.

Lizette Woodworth Reese

THE BUDDING BRONX

Der spring is sprung
Der grass is riz
I wonder where dem boidies is?

Der little boids is on der wing.
Ain't dat absoid?
Der little wings is on der boid!

Anon

PINK AZALEA

I feel as though
this bush were grown
especially for me.
I feel as though
I almost am
this little flowering tree.

Charlotte Zolotow

A PIPER

A piper in the streets today
Set up, and tuned, and started to play,
And away, away, away on the tide
Of his music we started; on every side
Doors and windows were opened wide,
And men left down their work and came,
And women with petticoats coloured like flame
And little bare feet that were blue with cold,
Went dancing back to the age of gold,
And all the world went gay, went gay,
For half an hour in the street today.

Seumas O'Sullivan

BIRD AND BEAST

Did any bird come flying
After Adam and Eve
When the door was shut against them
And they sat down to grieve?

I think not Eve's peacock,
Splendid to see.
And I think not Adam's eagle
But a dove maybe.

Did any beast come pushing
Through the thorny hedge?
Into the thorny, thistly world
Out from Eden's edge?

I think not a lion,
Though his strength is such,
But I think an innocent lamb
May have done as much.

Christina Rossetti

THE RAINBOW

I saw the lovely arch
    Of Rainbow span the sky,
        The gold sun burning
            As the rain swept by.

            In bright-ringed solitude
            The showery foliage shone
            One lovely moment,
            And the Bow was gone.

Walter de la Mare

TWO GOODLY KINGS

King David and King Solomon
    Lived merry, merry lives,
With many, many lady friends
    And many, many wives.

But when old age crept over them
    With many, many qualms,
King Solomon wrote the Proverbs
    And King David wrote the Psalms.

Anon

53

DADDY FELL INTO THE POND

Everyone grumbled. The sky was grey.
We had nothing to do and nothing to say.
We were nearing the end of a dismal day,
And there seemed to be nothing beyond,
     THEN
  Daddy fell into the pond!

And everyone's face grew merry and bright,
And Timothy danced for sheer delight.
"Give me the camera, quick, oh quick!
He's crawling out of the duckweed." Click!

Then the gardener suddenly slapped his knee,
And doubled up, shaking silently,
And the ducks all quacked as if they were daft,
And it sounded as if the old drake laughed.

O, there wasn't a thing that didn't respond
     WHEN
  Daddy fell into the pond!

Alfred Noyes

SOMETHING TOLD THE WILD GEESE

Something told the wild geese
It was time to go.
Though the fields lay golden
Something whispered — "Snow."
Leaves were green and stirring,
Berries, lustre-glossed,
But beneath warm feathers
Something cautioned, — "Frost."

All the sagging orchards
Steamed with amber spice,
But each wild breast stiffened
At remembered ice.
Something told the wild geese
It was time to fly —
Summer sun was on their wings,
Winter in their cry.

Rachel Field

BE LIKE THE BIRD

Be like the bird, who
Halting in his flight
On limb too slight
Feels it give way beneath him,
Yet sings
Knowing he hath wings.

Victor Hugo

FAITH

Ah . . . that's the reason
    a bird can sing,
On the darkest day.
    He believes in spring.

Douglas Molloch

THE DONKEY

When fishes flew and forests walked,
And figs grew upon thorn,
Some moment when the moon was blood,
Then surely I was born;

With monstrous head and sickening cry,
And ears like errant wings,
The devil's walking parody
On all four-footed things.

The tattered outlaw of the earth,
Of ancient crooked will;
Starve, scourge, deride me: I am dumb,
I keep my secret still.

Fools! For I also had my hour;
One far fierce hour and sweet:
There was a shout about my ears,
And palms before my feet.

G. K. Chesterton

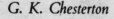

THEN

Twenty, forty, sixty, eighty,
A hundred years ago,
All through the night with lantern bright
The Watch trudged to and fro,
And little children snug abed
Would wake from dreams to hear —
"Two o' the morning by the clock,
And the stars a-shining clear!"
Or, when across the chimney-tops
Screamed shrill a north-east gale,
A faint and shaken voice would shout,
"Three! — and a storm of hail!"

Walter de la Mare

GOD BE IN MY HEAD

God be in my head
And in my understanding;

God be in my eyes
And in my looking;

God be in my mouth
And in my speaking;

God be in my heart
And in my thinking;

God be at my end
And at my departing.

The Sarum Missal

A PAVANE FOR THE NURSERY

Now touch the air softly,
Step gently. One two . . .
I'll love you till roses
Are robin's-egg blue;
I'll love you till gravel
Is eaten for bread,
And lemons are orange,
And lavender's red.

Now touch the air softly,
Swing gently the broom.
I'll love you till windows
Are all of a room;
And the table is laid,
And the table is bare,
And the ceiling reposes
On bottomless air.

I'll love you till Heaven
Rips the stars from his coat,
And the moon rows away in
A glass-bottomed boat;
And Orion steps down
Like a diver below,
And Earth is ablaze,
And Ocean aglow.

So touch the air softly,
And swing the broom high.
We will dust the grey mountains,
And sweep the blue sky;
And I'll love you as long
As the furrow the plough,
As However is Ever,
And Ever is Now.

William Jay Smith

THE BLACKBIRD

In the far corner
close by the swings,
every morning
a blackbird sings.

His bill's so yellow,
his coat's so black,
that he makes a fellow
whistle back.

Ann, my daughter,
thinks that he
sings for us two
especially.

Humbert Wolfe

THE WENDIGO

The Wendigo,
The Wendigo!
Its eyes are ice and indigo!
Its blood is rank and yellowish!
Its voice is hoarse and bellowish!
Its tentacles are slithery,
And scummy.
Slimy,
Leathery!
Its lips are hungry blubbery,
And smacky,
Sucky,
Rubbery!
The Wendigo,
The Wendigo!
I saw it just a friend ago!
Last night it lurked in Canada;
Tonight, on your veranada!
As you are lolling hammockwise
It contemplates you stomachwise.
You loll,
It contemplates,
It lollops.
The rest is merely gulps and gollops.

Ogden Nash

COTTAGE

When I live in a Cottage
I shall keep in my Cottage

Two different Dogs
Three creamy Cows
Four giddy Goats
Five pewter Pots
Six silver Spoons
Seven busy Beehives
Eight ancient Appletrees
Nine red Rosebushes
Ten teeming Teapots
Eleven chirping Chickens
Twelve cosy Cats
    with their kittenish Kittens
    and
One Blessed Baby in a Basket.

That's what I'll have when I live in my Cottage.

    Eleanor Farjeon

TO LADDIE

Whistle, Laddie, whistle,
Whistle when the dawn
Dances in the shadows
Gay-hearted as a fawn.

Whistle, Laddie, whistle,
Whistle merrily;
Whistle for the red-wing
And the chickadee.

Whistle, Laddie, whistle,
While the fireflies spark;
Truer, clearer, louder,
Whistle through the dark.

Anne Robinson

LEAN OUT OF THE WINDOW

Lean out of the window,
Goldenhair,
I heard you singing
A merry air.

My book is closed,
I read no more,
Watching the fire dance
On the floor.

I have left my book:
I have left my room:
For I heard you singing
Through the gloom,

Singing and singing
A merry air.
Lean out of the window,
Goldenhair.

James Joyce

ADVICE TO SMALL CHILDREN

Eat no green apples or you'll droop,
Be careful not to get the croup,
Avoid the chicken-pox and such,
And don't fall out of windows much.

Edward Anthony

THE BELLS OF HEAVEN

'Twould ring the bells of heaven
The wildest peal for years,
If Parson lost his senses
And people came to theirs,
And he and they together
Knelt down with angry prayers
For tamed and shabby tigers
And dancing dogs and bears,
And wretched, blind pit ponies
And little hunted hares.

Ralph Hodgson

TREES

Trees are the kindest things I know;
They do no harm, they simply grow,

And spread a shade for sleepy cows,
And gather birds among their boughs.

They give us fruit in leaves above,
And wood to make our houses of,

And leaves to burn on Hallowe'en,
And in the spring new buds of green.

They are the first when day's begun
To touch the beams of morning sun,

They are the last to hold the light
When evening changes into night,

And when a moon floats on the sky
They hum a drowsy lullaby

Of sleepy children long ago . . .
Trees are the kindest things I know.

Harry Behn

THE MOUSE IN THE WAINSCOT

Hush, Suzanne!
Don't lift your cup.
That breath you heard
Is a mouse getting up.

As the mist that steams
From your milk as you sup,
So soft is the sound
Of a mouse getting up.

There! did you hear
His feet pitter-patter,
Lighter than tipping
Of beads in a platter,

And then like a shower
On the window pane
The little feet scampering
Back again?

O falling of feather!
O drift of a leaf!
The mouse in the wainscot
Is dropping asleep.

Ian Serraillier

A PRAYER

Lord, make me an instrument of Thy peace;
Where there is hatred, let me sow love;
Where there is injury, pardon;
Where there is discord, union;
Where there is doubt, faith;
Where there is despair, hope;
Where there is darkness, light;
Where there is sadness, joy.

St Francis of Assisi

BOATS SAIL ON THE RIVERS

Boats sail on the rivers,
    And ships sail on the seas;
But clouds that sail across the sky
    Are prettier far than these.

There are bridges on the rivers,
    As pretty as you please;
But the bow that bridges heaven,
    And overtops the trees,
And builds a road from earth to sky
    Is prettier far than these.

Christina Rossetti

THE VOWELS

We are very little creatures
All of different voice and features.
One of us in *glass* is set,
One of us you'll find in *jet*,
T'other you may see in *tin*,
And the fourth, a *box* within.
If the fifth you would pursue,
It can never fly from *you*.

> *Jonathan Swift*

BEAUTY ETERNAL

Today I saw
 a butterfly,
The first-born
 of the spring
Sunning itself
 upon a bank —
A lovely
 tawny thing.

I saw
 a dandelion, too,
As golden
 as the sun;
And these will
 still be beautiful
When all the
 wars are done.

> *Teresa Hooley*

MEAN SONG

Snickles and podes,
Ribble and grodes:
That's what I wish you.

A nox in the groot,
A root in the stoot
And a gock in the forbeshaw, too.

Keep out of sight
For fear that I might
Grom you a gravely snave.

Don't show your face
Around any place
Or you'll get one flack snack in the bave.

Eve Merriam

73

SUNNING

Old Dog lay in the summer sun
Much too lazy to rise and run.
He flapped an ear
At a buzzing fly;
He winked a half-opened
Sleepy eye;
He scratched himself
On an itching spot;
As he dozed on the porch
When the sun was hot.

He whimpered a bit
From force of habit,
While he lazily dreamed
Of chasing a rabbit.

But Old Dog happily lay in the sun,
Much too lazy to rise and run.

James S. Tippett

WHERE GO THE BOATS?

Dark brown is the river,
Golden is the sand.
It flows along for ever,
With trees on either hand.

Green leaves a-floating,
Castles of the foam,
Boats of mine a-boating —
Where will all come home?

On goes the river
And out past the mill,
Away down the valley,
Away down the hill.

Away down the river,
A hundred miles or more,
Other little children
Shall bring my boats ashore.

Robert Louis Stevenson

I AM ROSE

I am Rose my eyes are blue.
I am Rose and who are you?
I am Rose and when I sing
I am Rose like anything.

Gertrude Stein

KINGS CAME RIDING

Kings came riding
  One, two and three,
Over the desert
  And over the sea.

One in a ship
  With a silver mast;
The fishermen wondered
  As he went past.

One on a horse
  With a saddle of gold;
The children came running
  To behold.

One came walking
  Over the sand,
With a casket of treasure
  Held in his hand.

All the people
  Said "Where go they?"
But the kings went forward
  All through the day.

Night came on
  As those kings went by;
They shone like the gleaming
  Stars in the sky.

Charles Williams

WHO LOVES THE RAIN

Who loves the rain
And loves his home
And looks on life with quiet eyes
Him will I follow through the storm;
And at his hearth-fire keep me warm;
Nor hell nor heaven shall that soul surprise,
Who loves the rain,
And loves his home,
And looks on life with quiet eyes.

Frances Wells Shaw

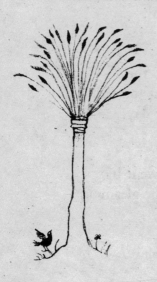

BROOMS

On stormy days
When the wind is high
Tall trees are brooms
Sweeping the sky.

They swish their branches
In buckets of rain,
And swash and sweep it
Blue again.

Dorothy Aldis

78

MEASLES IN THE ARK

The night it was horribly dark,
The measles broke out in the Ark;
Little Japheth, and Shem, and all the young Hams,
Were screaming at once for potatoes and clams.
And "What shall I do?" said poor Mrs Noah,
"All alone by myself in this terrible shower?
I know what I'll do: I'll step down in the hold,
And wake up a lioness grim and old,
And tie her close to the children's door
And give her a ginger-cake to roar
At the top of her voice for an hour or more;
And I'll tell the children to cease their din,
Or I'll let that grim old party in,
To stop their squeazles and likewise their measles."
She practised this with the greatest success:
She was everyone's grandmother, I guess.

Susan Coolidge

WILD GEESE

I heard the wild geese flying
    In the dead of the night
With beat of wings and crying
I heard the wild geese flying,
And dreams in my heart sighing
    Followed their northward flight
I heard the wild geese flying
    In the dead of the night.

Elinor Chipp

FOUR DUCKS ON A POND

Four ducks on a pond,
A grass-bank beyond,
A blue sky of spring,
White clouds on the wing:
What a little thing
To remember for years —
To remember with tears!

William Allingham

LITTLE THINGS

Little things, that run, and quail,
And die in silence and despair!

Little things, that fight, and fail,
And fall on sea, and earth, and air!

All trapped and frightened little things,
The mouse, the coney, hear our prayer!

As we forgive those done to us,
— The lamb, the linnet, and the hare —

Forgive us all our trespasses,
Little creatures, everywhere.

James Stephens

WHO HATH A BOOK

Who hath a book
Hath friends at hand,
And gold and gear
At his command;
And rich estates,
If he but look,
Are held by him
Who hath a book.

Who hath a book
Hath but to read
And he may be
A king, indeed.
His kingdom is
His inglenook —
All this is his
Who hath a book.

Wilbur D. Nesbit

WINDY NIGHTS

Whenever the moon and stars are set,
Whenever the wind is high,
All night long in the dark and wet,
A man goes riding by.
Late in the night when the fires are out,
Why does he gallop and gallop about?

Whenever the trees are crying aloud,
And ships are tossed at sea,
By, on the highway, low and loud,
By at the gallop goes he.
By at the gallop he goes, and then
By he comes back at the gallop again.

Robert Louis Stevenson

GRANNY

Through every nook and every cranny
The wind blew in on poor old Granny;
Around her knees, into each ear
(And up her nose as well, I fear).

All through the night the wind grew worse,
It nearly made the vicar curse.
The top had fallen off the steeple
Just missing him (and other people).

It blew on man; it blew on beast.
It blew on nun; it blew on priest.
It blew the wig off Auntie Fanny —
But most of all, it blew on Granny!!

Spike Milligan

WINTER IS PAST

For, lo, the winter is past,
The rain is over and gone;
The flowers appear on the earth;
The time of the singing of birds is come,
And the voice of the turtle is heard in our land;
The fig tree putteth forth her green figs,
And the vines with the tender grape
Give a good smell.

From the "Song of Solomon"
The Holy Bible

SEAL LULLABY

Oh! hush thee, my baby,
the night is behind us,
And black are the waters
that sparkled so green.
The moon, o'er the combers,
looks downward to find us
At rest in the hollows
that rustle between.

Where billow meets billow,
then soft be thy pillow,
Ah, weary wee flipperling,
curl at thy ease!
The storm shall not wake thee,
nor shark overtake thee,
Asleep in the arms
of the slow-swinging seas.

Rudyard Kipling

QUEEN NEFERTITI

Spin a coin, spin a coin,
All fall down;
Queen Nefertiti
Stalks through the town.

Over the pavements
Her feet go clack;
Her legs are as tall
As a chimney stack.

Her fingers flicker
Like snakes in the air;
The walls slit open
At her green-eyed stare.

Her voice is thin
As the ghosts of bees;
She will crumble your bones
She will make your blood freeze.

Spin a coin, spin a coin,
All fall down;
Queen Nefertiti
Stalks through the town.

Anon

THE SNARE

I hear a sudden cry of pain!
There is a rabbit in a snare:
Now I hear the cry again,
But I cannot tell from where.

But I cannot tell from where
He is calling out for aid;
Crying on the frightened air,
Making everything afraid.

Making everything afraid,
Wrinkling up his little face,
As he cries again for aid;
And I cannot find the place!

And I cannot find the place
Where his paw is in the snare:
Little one! Oh, little one!
I am searching everywhere!

James Stephens

ME

As long as I live
I shall always be
My Self — and no other,
Just me.

Like a tree —
Willow, elder,
Aspen, thorn,
Or cypress forlorn.

Like a flower,
For its hour —
Primrose, or pink,
Or a violet —
Sunned by the sun,
And with dewdrops wet.

Always just me,
Till the day come on
When I leave this body.
It's all then done,
And the spirit within it
Is gone.

Walter de la Mare

THE FOX RHYME

Aunt was on the garden seat
Enjoying a wee nap and
Along came a fox! teeth
Closed with a snap and
He's running to the woods with her
A-dangle and a-flap and —
Run, uncle, run
And see what has happened!

Ian Serraillier

THE FROG

What a wonderful bird the frog are —
When he stand he sit almost;
When he hop he fly almost.
He ain't got no sense hardly;
He ain't got no tail hardly neither.
When he sit, he sit on what he ain't got almost.

Anon

NOAH AND THE RABBIT

"No land," said Noah.
"There-is-not-any-land.
Oh Rabbit, Rabbit, can't you understand?"

But Rabbit shook his head:
"Say it again," he said;
"And slowly, please.
No good brown earth for burrows,
And no trees;
No wastes where vetch and rabbit-parsley grows,
No brakes, no bushes and no turnip rows,
No holt, no upland, meadowland or weald,
No tangled hedgerow and no playtime field?"

"No land at all — just water," Noah replied,
And Rabbit sighed.
"For always, Noah?" he whispered. "Will there be
Nothing henceforth for ever but the sea?
Or will there come a day
When the green earth will call me back to play?"

Noah bowed his head:
"Some day . . . some day," he said.

Hugh Chesterman

SILVER

Slowly, silently, now the moon
Walks the night in her silver shoon;
This way and that she peers and sees
Silver fruit upon silver trees;
One by one the casements catch
Her beams beneath the silvery thatch;
Couched in his kennel like a log,
With paws of silver sleeps the dog;
From their shadowy cote the white
                              breasts peep
Of doves in a silver-feathered sleep;
A harvest mouse goes scampering by,
With silver claws and silver eye;
And moveless fish in the water gleam,
By silver reeds in a silver stream.

Walter de la Mare

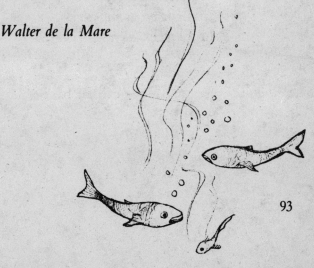

93

INNOCENCE

I saw a donkey
One day old,
His head was too big
For his neck to hold;
His legs were shaky
And long and loose,
They rocked and staggered
And weren't much use.

He tried to gambol
And frisk a bit,
But he wasn't sure
Of the trick of it.
His queer little coat
Was soft and grey
And curled at his neck
In a lovely way.

His face was wistful
And left no doubt
That he felt life needed
Some thinking about.
So he blundered round
In venturesome quest
And then lay flat
On the ground to rest.

He looked so little and weak and slim,
I prayed the world might be good to him.

Anon

WORDS

Bright is the ring of words
When the right man rings them,
Fair the fall of songs
When the singer sings them.
Still they are carolled and said —
On wings they are carried —
After the singer is dead
And the maker buried.

Robert Louis Stevenson

THE SWALLOW

Fly away, fly away, over the sea,
   Sun loving swallow, for summer is done.
Come again, come again, come back to me,
Bringing the summer and bringing the sun.

Christina Rossetti

I ONCE HAD A SWEET LITTLE DOLL . . .

I once had a sweet little doll, dears,
    The prettiest doll in the world;
Her cheeks were so red and so white, dears,
    And her hair was so charmingly curled.

But I lost my poor little doll, dears,
    As I played in the heath one day;
And I cried for her more than a week, dears,
    But I never could find where she lay.

I found my poor little doll, dears,
    As I played in the heath one day;
Folk say she is terribly changed, dears,
    For her paint is all washed away,

And her arm trodden off by cows, dears,
    And her hair not the least bit curled;
Yet for old sakes' sake she is still, dears,
    The prettiest doll in the world.

Charles Kingsley

GYPSY JANE

She had cornflowers in her hair
As she came up the lane;
"What may be your name, my dear?"
"O, sir, Gypsy Jane."

"You are berry-brown, my dear."
"That, sir, well may be,
For I live more than half the year,
Under tent or tree."

Shine, Sun! Blow, Wind!
Fall gently, Rain!
The year's declined, be soft and kind.
Kind to Gypsy Jane.

William Brighty Rands

ANCIENT HISTORY

I hope the old Romans
Had painful abdomens.

I hope that the Greeks
Had toothache for weeks.

I hope the Egyptians
Had chronic conniptions.

I hope that the Arabs
Were bitten by scarabs.

I hope that the Vandals
Had thorns in their sandals.

I hope that the Persians
Had gout in all versions.

I hope that the Medes
Were kicked by their steeds.

They started the fuss
And left it to us!

Arthur Guiterman

THE KING'S HORSES

The King of Cathay has eleven fine horses:
They snort with delight as they hear him approach.
One takes him riding the meadows at sunrise,
Six are the Chestnuts that draw his gold coach;
One is a charger — oh! blacker than midnight,
Another is glossy, mahogany-skinned;
One is a stallion, grey as a raincloud,
And one is an Arab that flies with the wind.

Clive Sansom

SPRING RAIN

The storm came up so very quick
It couldn't have been quicker.
I should have brought my hat along,
I should have brought my slicker.

My hair is wet my feet are wet,
I couldn't be much wetter.
I fell into a river once
But this is even better.

Marchette Chute

A ROBIN REDBREAST IN A CAGE

A robin redbreast in a cage
Puts all Heaven in a rage.
A dove-house filled with doves and pigeons
Shudders Hell thro' all its regions.
A dog starved at the master's gate
Predicts the ruin of the State.
A horse misused upon the road
Calls to Heaven for human blood.
Each outcry of the hunted hare
A fibre from the brain does tear.
A skylark wounded in the wing,
A cherubim does cease to sing.

William Blake

REQUIEM

Under the wide and starry sky
Dig the grave and let me lie.
Glad did I live and gladly die,
And I laid me down with a will.

This be the verse you grave for me:
"Here he lies where he longed to be;
Home is the sailor, home from sea,
And the hunter home from the hill."

Robert Louis Stevenson

LAST SONG

To the Sun
Who has shone
All day,
To the Moon
Who has gone
Away,

To the milk-white
Silk-white,
Lily-white Star,
A fond good-night
Wherever you are.

James Guthrie

HOUSE BLESSING

Bless the four corners of this house,
    And be the lintel blest;
And bless the hearth and bless the board
    And bless each place of rest;
And bless the door that opens wide
    To stranger as to kin;
And bless each crystal window-pane
    That lets the starlight in;
And bless the rooftree overhead
    And every sturdy wall.
The peace of man, the peace of God,
    The peace of Love on all!

Arthur Guiterman

ACKNOWLEDGEMENTS

For permission to use copyright material we thank the
following

Angus & Robertson Publishers – *The Magic Pudding* poem by
Norman Lindsay is reprinted with the permission of Angus
& Robertson Publishers. © Janet Glad.

The Blackie Publishing Group Ltd, Scotland, for "Who's
In?" by Elizabeth Fleming from *The Creepie Stool*.

Basil Blackwell Publisher, Oxford, for "Little Girl" by Rose
Fyleman and "Last Song" by James Guthrie.

Jonathan Cape Ltd and the Estate of Teresa Hooley for
"Beauty Eternal" from the *Selected Poems*.

Marchette Chute for "Spring Rain", reprinted from *Around
and About* by permission of the author. Copyright 1957, E. P.
Dutton.

Miss D. E. Collins and A. P. Watt Ltd for "The Donkey"
and "A Christmas Carol" by G. K. Chesterton.

Curtis Brown Ltd, New York, for "The Wendigo" from *The
Private Dining Room and Other Verses* by Ogden Nash
published by Little Brown, New York, copyright © Ogden
Nash 1952.

Edward J. Dietrich for "A Little Song of Life" from the
Selected Poems of Lizette Woodworth Reese, Rinehart & Co.
Inc., 1926.

Eyre & Spottiswoode (Publishers Ltd) – extracts from the
Authorized King James Version of the Bible, which is Crown
Copyright, are reproduced by permission of Eyre &
Spottiswoode, Her Majesty's Printers, London.

Norma Farnes for
"Granny" from *Silly Verse for Kids* by Spike Milligan,
published by Puffin Books.

Harcourt Brace Jovanovich, Inc. for "Lessons" from *Windy
Morning*, copyright 1953 by Harry Behn, renewed 1981 by
Alice Behn Goebel, Pamela Behn Adam, Prescott Behn and

The National Trust, Macmillan, London Limited and A. P.
Watt Ltd for the Chapter-heading verses from "The White
Seal" from *The Jungle Book* by Rudyard Kipling.
G. P. Putnam's Sons for "Brooms" by Dorothy Aldis from
Everything and Anything by Dorothy Aldis, copyright
1925-1927, copyright renewed 1953-1955 by Dorothy Aldis.
Marian Reiner for "For a Bird" from *The Moon and a Star
and Other Poems* by Myra Cohn Livingston, copyright © 1965
by Myra Cohn Livingston. Reprinted by permission of
Marian Reiner for the author.
Penelope Rieu for "Cat's Funeral" by E. V. Rieu.
Louise H. Sclove for "Ancient History" by Arthur Guiterman
from *Gaily the Troubadour*, copyright 1936 and "The House
Blessing" by Arthur Guiterman from *The Mirthful Lyre*,
copyright 1918.
Ian Serraillier for "The Fox Rhyme" and "The Mouse in the
Wainscot" both © 1950 Ian Serraillier.
The Society of Authors — as the literary representative of the
Estate of James Joyce for "Lean Out of the Window" from
Chamber Music by James Joyce and the Estate of Richard le
Gallienne for "I Meant to Do My Work Today" by Richard
le Gallienne; on behalf of the copyright owner, Mrs Iris
Wise, for "Little Things" and "The Snare" by James
Stephens.
William Jay Smith for "A Pavane for the Nursery" from *The
Traveler's Tree: New and Selected Poems* by William Jay Smith,
published 1980 by Persea Books, copyright © 1957, 1980 by
William Jay Smith.
World's Work Ltd for "Animal Store", "General Store" and
"If Once You Have Slept on an Island" by Rachel Field
from *Taxis and Toadstools*. Copyright © 1926 Doubleday &
Co. Inc. Copyright © 1924 by Yale Publishing Co. Copyright
1926 by Crowell Publishing Co. First published in G. B. in
1962. All rights reserved.
The publishers have made every effort to trace copyright
holders, in some cases without success. We would be grateful
to hear from any copyright holders not here acknowledged.

INDEX to AUTHORS, first lines and *titles*